HAROLD GETS AN F

TOO MUCH FUN CAN COME AT A PRICE

Written & Illustrated by Calvin Reynolds

Book design and cover by Calvin Reynolds

Harold Get An "F"

Printed in the United States of America
ISBN: 978-0-9986630-4-3 (Hardcover)

Published in 2020 by Concepts Redefined, an imprint of Calvin Reynolds
All rights reserved.

Harold Get An "F"

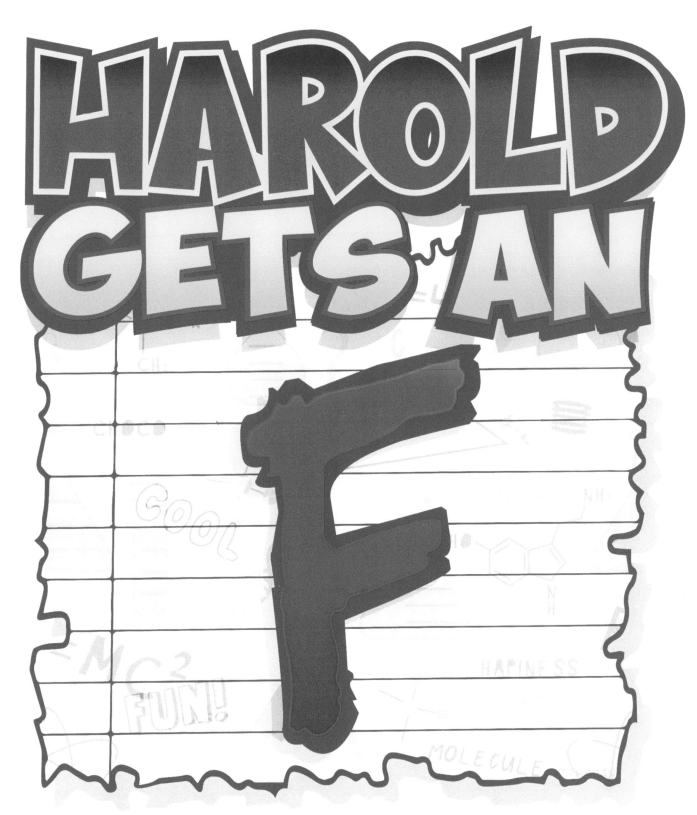

HAROLD GETS AN F

Written & Illustrated by Calvin Reynolds

Meet Harold.
He's a super-smart 5th grader who loves going to school and making good grades.

His favorite subject is
Science.

Harold has a big
Science quiz coming
up on Friday.

He's pretty confident
that he'll pass the test with
flying colors.

On Monday when Harold got home from school, instead of studying, he decided to play video games all evening.

9

On Tuesday,
Harold had so much fun
playing sports with his
friends.

He also made time to play with his favorite toys.

On Wednesday, Harold flew his kite.

On Thursday, Harold went fishing with his pet dog.

Harold even made time to go skate boarding.

He had so much FUN!

When Friday arrived,
Harold strutted into
class ready to take
his Science test.

While taking the test, Harold looked a little confused.

When time was up,
Mrs. London collected
all of the tests.

Mrs. London, took her time and graded everyone's test.

When the bell rang, she
handed each child
their results.

When Harold got his test, he was shocked!

He had a big fat F.
Harold flunked his test.

Harold was confused and asked his teacher, "What happened? Why did I get an F?"

The teacher asked
Harold,
"Did you study, because
you answered all
the questions wrong?"

Harold realized that instead
of making time to study,
he chose to spend time
enjoying his favorite hobbies.

"I hope you've learned a valuable lesson from this. Lucky for you, there will be a makeup test on Monday." Mrs. London said.

Harold's eyes opened wide with excitement! "Awesome!" He responded.

Over the weekend, Harold made time to study. When he took the test on Monday, he got an **A⁺**.

Harold learned that there's a time to work, and there's a time to play. Being responsible is important.

THE END

About the Author / Illustrator

Calvin Reynolds is a professional
illustrator/graphic designer and award-winning children's book
author from Tampa Bay, Florida.
His desire to inspire children has led him to create
and illustrate stories that capture their imagination and foster a
love of reading and art.
See more of Calvin's books and illustrations at
amazon.com/author/calvinreynolds
www.jaycethebee.com
www.conceptsredefined.net